Cider

Honey

AUTUMN
HARVEST

by Alvin Tresselt

Illustrated by Roger Duvoisin

LOTHROP, LEE & SHEPARD CO. NEW YORK

17 18 19 20

In the late summer evening sang the katydids.

Katydid...katydidn't...katydid...katydidn't.

In the treetops, in the thickets, in the grass...

While the wise old country people said, "Six weeks till frost."

Now the first autumn chill touched the summer night.

Now sleeping birds stirred in the cool night breeze, for soon would come their long flight south.

Katydid...katydidn't...katydid...katydidn't sang the katydids as the August moon climbed the eastern sky.

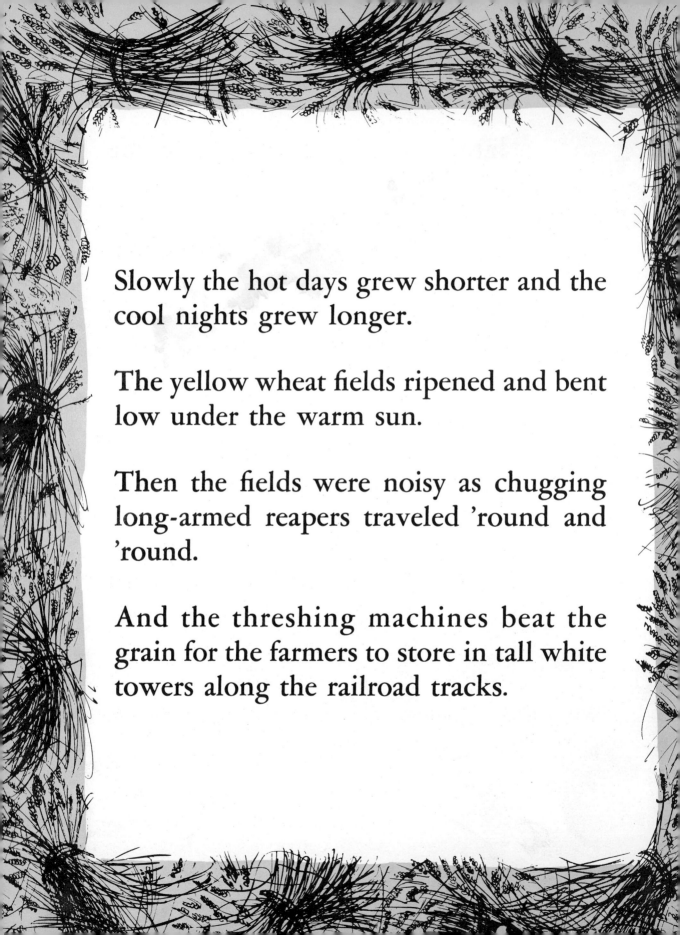

Slowly the hot days grew shorter and the cool nights grew longer.

The yellow wheat fields ripened and bent low under the warm sun.

Then the fields were noisy as chugging long-armed reapers traveled 'round and 'round.

And the threshing machines beat the grain for the farmers to store in tall white towers along the railroad tracks.

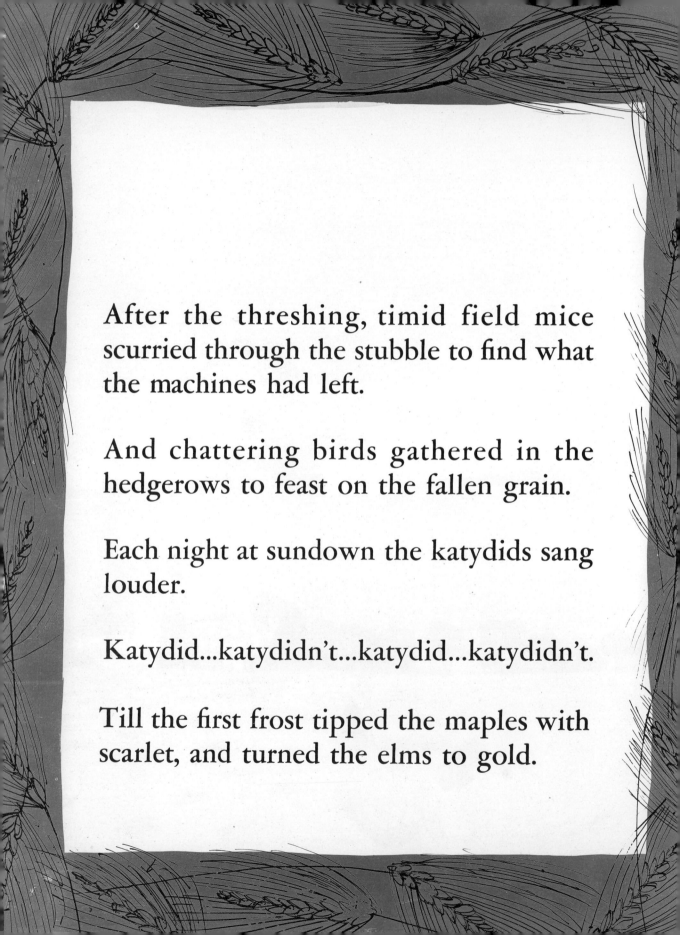

After the threshing, timid field mice scurried through the stubble to find what the machines had left.

And chattering birds gathered in the hedgerows to feast on the fallen grain.

Each night at sundown the katydids sang louder.

Katydid...katydidn't...katydid...katydidn't.

Till the first frost tipped the maples with scarlet, and turned the elms to gold.

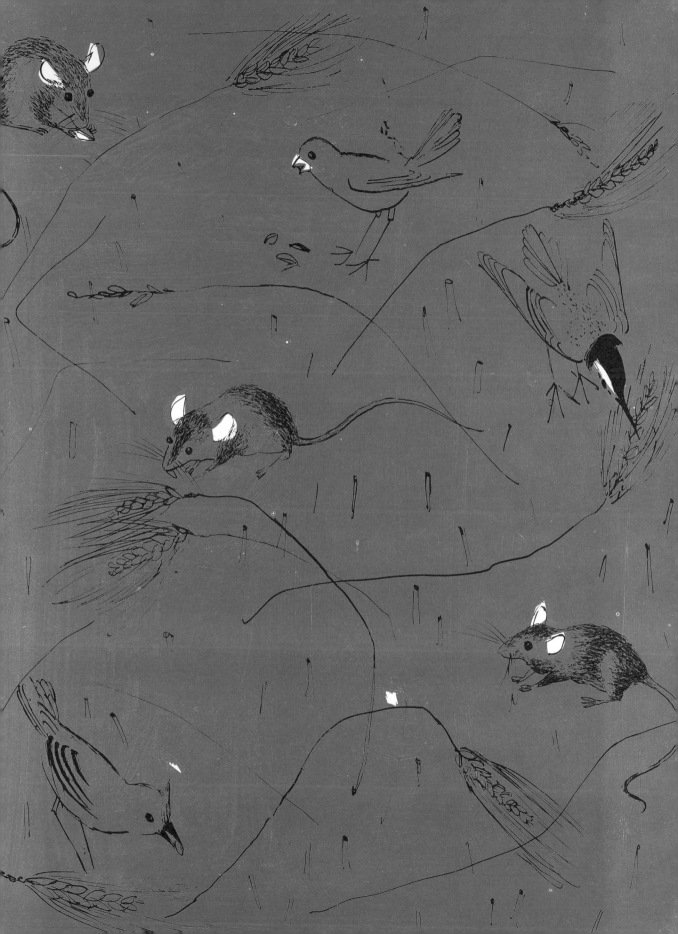

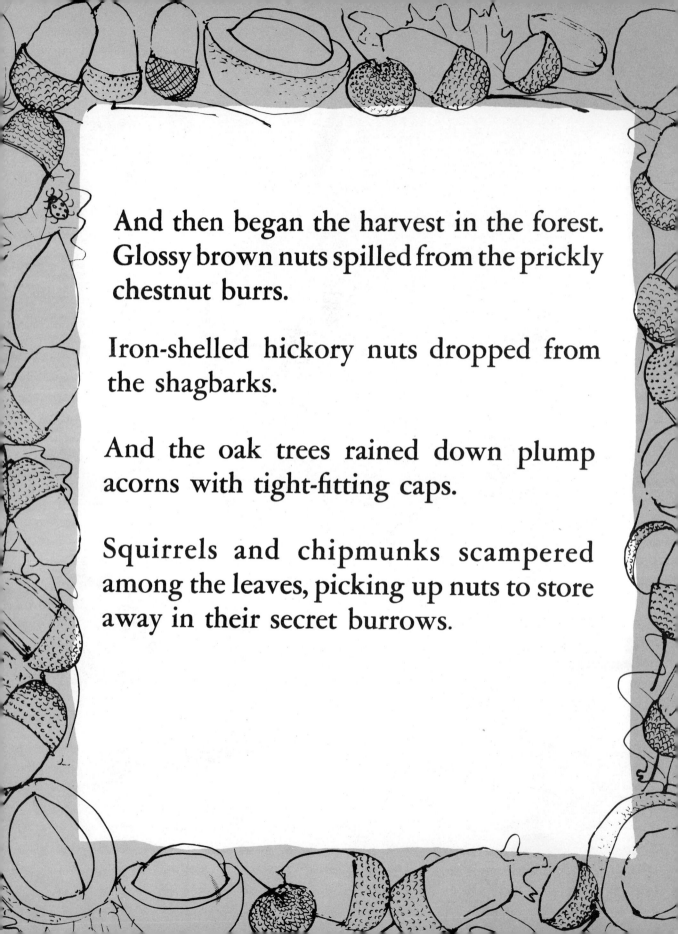

And then began the harvest in the forest. Glossy brown nuts spilled from the prickly chestnut burrs.

Iron-shelled hickory nuts dropped from the shagbarks.

And the oak trees rained down plump acorns with tight-fitting caps.

Squirrels and chipmunks scampered among the leaves, picking up nuts to store away in their secret burrows.

The children on their way from school hiked through the ragged forest.

They trampled on the dry sticks and leaves, and their laughter sparkled in the golden autumn sunlight.

Then they crossed the pastures, picking stiff bunches of goldenrod and purple asters to take home.

They split the fat bumply milkweed pods, and a thousand silky parachutes floated lightly over the brown weedy fields.

In the orchard ladders leaned against the trees heavy with fruit.

And the children helped the nimble pickers fill the wagons with shiny apples and golden pears.

They listened to the gossipy birds strung along telephone wires, waiting to start their autumn flight.

And high in the sky came a faraway honk of wild geese as they moved slowly southward in V-shaped flocks.

One night a heavy frost whitened the countryside, and the katydids stopped singing for another year.

The farmer watched the autumn stars of Orion's belt twinkle brightly in the clear night sky.

He took a deep breath of the frosty air, then went out to the barn to make sure the doors were shut tight.

In the misty morning light the trees burned with bright red and yellow and gold, and the fields and roof-tops glistened with white frost crystals.

But the day grew warm as the Indian Summer sun broke through the haze, and squeaky cricket chirps sounded from the frost-bitten grass.

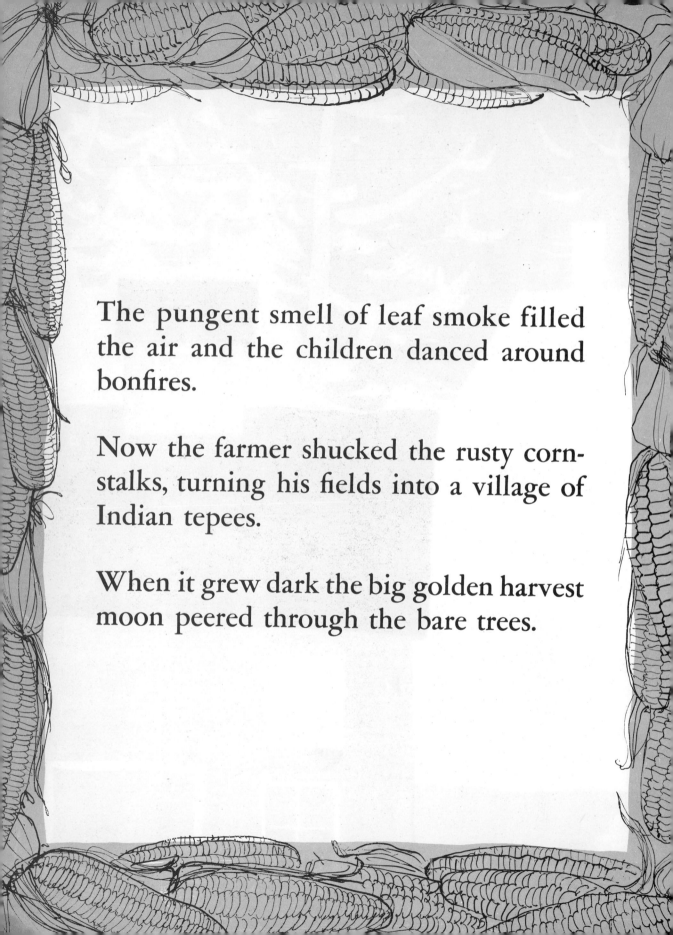

The pungent smell of leaf smoke filled the air and the children danced around bonfires.

Now the farmer shucked the rusty cornstalks, turning his fields into a village of Indian tepees.

When it grew dark the big golden harvest moon peered through the bare trees.

Then one night Hallowe'en pumpkins grinned from fenceposts, and children shivered with delight as they ran past in their funny clothes.

One day the wind shook down the last of the autumn leaves, and the frost sank deep into the ground.

Fragile ghosts of goldenrod and Queen Anne's lace stood with the brown mullen stalks along the roadside.

Neat grey juncos and saucy little nuthatches begged for crumbs in the dooryard.

Now the farmer rested in his big easy chair by the fire.

His harvest was gathered, and he smoked his pipe as he watched the children playing with their cousins.

The visiting aunts and uncles bustled around, exchanging news and helping with the Thanksgiving dinner.

From the kitchen came the rich smells of roasting turkey and mince pies.

At last the feast was ready. There was room for everyone around the stretched-out table and everyone had come home for Thanksgiving.

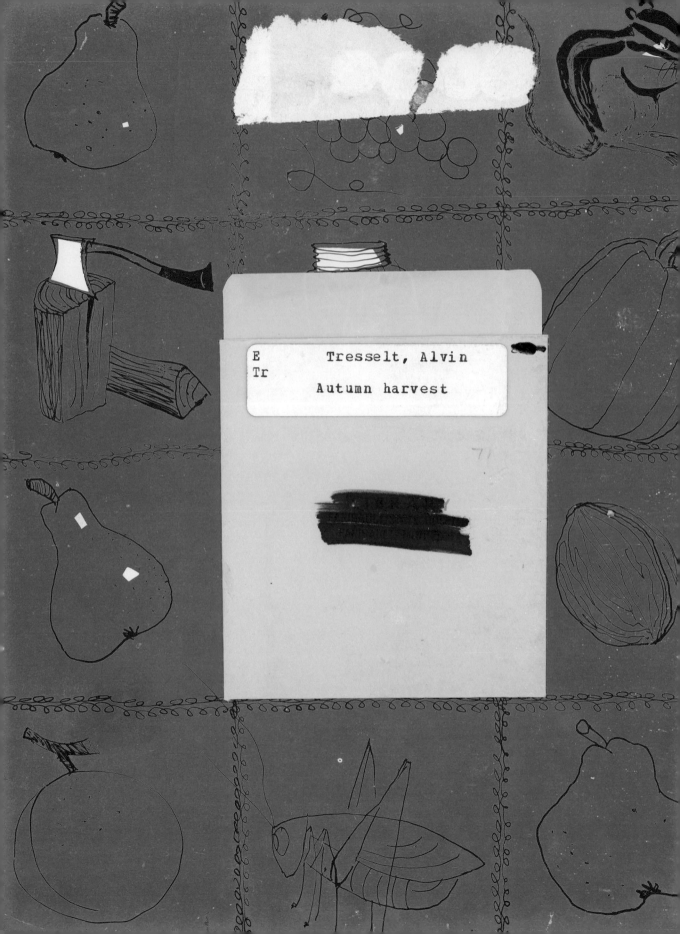